2 SLIM & FIT

8 SEVEN-DAY PLAN

10 RAW FOODS & SALADS

24 SOUPS & STEWS

32 MAINLY VEGETABLES

46 SWEET & FRUITY

54 POWER DRINKS & SHAKES

Slim
healthy and beautiful
& fit

HOW TO ACHIEVE YOUR AIM

We all want to be slim and healthy and look good. And we all know that traditional diets are no help. All that is required is a carefully chosen eating plan consisting of equally carefully prepared dishes that contain a minimum of fat. Then make sure you get enough exercise and don't over-tax your body with too much alcohol or tobacco.

VITAMINS–NATURE'S MIRACLES

We cannot see vitamins, and yet we cannot survive without them – in fact, we need a certain amount of them every day. These tiny little miracles provide no calories; in fact, they are our body's "labourers". They are involved in every single metabolic process, are essential for the reproduction of cells, blood, and bones, and strengthen the immune system. In short: vitamins keep us healthy and happy. Not enough of them, and we soon start to feel weak and fall ill.

MINIATURE IMMIGRANTS

Our body cannot make the most important

vitamins; it relies on a regular supply from outside. If we have the full requirement of a particular vitamin, the reserves will last between a few days and two years, depending on the vitamin in question. Whether a vitamin is fat- or water-soluble determines just how long the reserves last. Vitamins are divided into two groups: fat-soluble vitamins A, D, E, and K, and the water-soluble ones, vitamins B and C. Our body can store fat-soluble vitamins; any excess is simply excreted, so it is possible to have too much of a good thing. Water-soluble vitamins cannot be stored for so long. Vitamin C, for example, needs to be replenished on a daily basis.

Healthy Mites

We have read just how important these invisible miracles are. So what to do? Easy: enjoy plenty of variety. Fruit and vegetables, wholemeal grains and cereals, milk and dairy products provide a good supply of vitamins. However, most diets do not contain sufficient variety, which means that they are unlikely to provide all of the vitamins we require. Think about your lifestyle. Smokers, for instance, require extra vitamins, as do expectant and nursing mothers, athletes, and invalids.

Your Daily Requirement is Provided by

Vitamin	Food
A	60g (2oz) carrots or 340g (12oz) apricots
D	250g (9oz) mushrooms or 215g (7½oz) redfish
E	200g (7oz) salsify or 21g (¾oz) sunflower oil
K	75g (3oz) broccoli or 20g (¾oz) spinach
B₁	400g (14oz) peas or 125g (4oz) lean pork chop
B₂	450g (1lb) salmon or 800g (1¾lb) broccoli
B₆	175g (6oz) salmon or 600g (1¾lb) green beans
B₁₂	60g (2oz) beef or 200g (7oz) yoghurt
Niacin	180g (6½oz) oyster mushrooms or 125g (5oz) liver
Folic acid	200g (7oz) spinach or 160g (5½oz) brussel sprouts
Pantothenic acid	300g (10oz) mushrooms or 380g (13½oz) watermelon
Biotin	100g (3½oz) green beans or 75g (3oz) fennel
C	60g (2oz) pepper (capsicum) or 150g (5oz) orange

In order to stay fit and healthy, aim to obtain your daily requirement of vitamins and minerals from the food you eat and liquids you drink (see chart above).

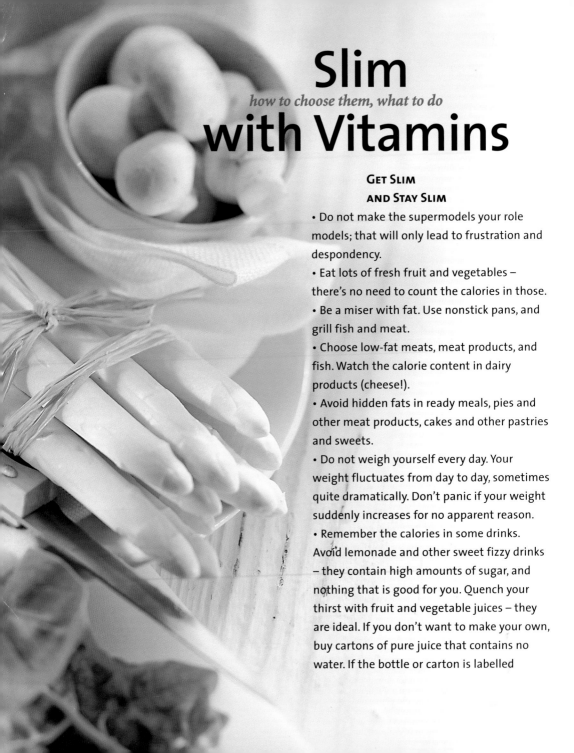

Slim

how to choose them, what to do

with Vitamins

GET SLIM
AND STAY SLIM

• Do not make the supermodels your role models; that will only lead to frustration and despondency.

• Eat lots of fresh fruit and vegetables – there's no need to count the calories in those.

• Be a miser with fat. Use nonstick pans, and grill fish and meat.

• Choose low-fat meats, meat products, and fish. Watch the calorie content in dairy products (cheese!).

• Avoid hidden fats in ready meals, pies and other meat products, cakes and other pastries and sweets.

• Do not weigh yourself every day. Your weight fluctuates from day to day, sometimes quite dramatically. Don't panic if your weight suddenly increases for no apparent reason.

• Remember the calories in some drinks. Avoid lemonade and other sweet fizzy drinks – they contain high amounts of sugar, and nothing that is good for you. Quench your thirst with fruit and vegetable juices – they are ideal. If you don't want to make your own, buy cartons of pure juice that contains no water. If the bottle or carton is labelled

"Nectar" or "Fruit drink", it contains lots of water and sugar.

SENSITIVE SOULS

Vitamins want to be treated with care! They cannot cope with light, air or heat, and so the following rules should be observed – especially in the case of fruit and vegetables:

* use as soon as possible
* if you need to store them, keep them cool and dark
* do not peel or chop until just before cooking
* wash as quickly as possible
* wash first, then chop or slice so that water-soluble vitamins do not leach out
* eat as many raw vegetables as possible
* steam fruit and vegetables under a tightly fitting lid, in their own juices or cook in a tiny amount of liquid
* serve as soon as possible.

It is worth investing in a steamer or a steamer insert. The main thing to remember is to use only a small amount of water. Place the vegetables in the steamer insert, then place the insert in or over the saucepan, cover with a lid and cook over a medium heat.

WHAT DESTROYS WHICH VITAMINS

VITAMIN	MAIN ENEMIES
A	light, air
D	reasonably resilient vitamin
E	light, air, heat
K	reasonably resilient vitamin
B_1	heat, water
B_2	light, water
B_6	heat, cold, water
B_{12}	light, air, water
Niacin	water
Folic acid	heat, light, water (very sensitive)
Pantothenic acid	heat, acid, water
Biotin	water
C	heat, light, air, water

IMPORTANT: Do not leave newly bought fruit and vegetables unwrapped or at room temperature for longer than absolutely necessary.

RECOMMENDATION: Use organic produce wherever possible. If you wish to avoid genetically modified (GM) foods, read any labels with care and select certified organic produce, as this is not produced from GM ingredients.

VITAMINS FOR BETTER HEALTH

VITAMIN	GOOD SOURCES
A	green-leafed vegetables, yellow and red fruits and vegetables, eggs, butter, liver
D	liver, meat, milk, fish, eggs, mushrooms
E	vegetable fats (especially wheatgerm, nettle and sunflower oils, cabbage, peppers (capsicum), spinach, salsify, avocados, cereals/grains, nuts, pulses
K	green vegetables, cereals/grains, milk, meat
B_1	bean and seed sprouts, pulses, cereals (wholemeal), potatoes, sunflower seeds, egg yolk, pork, yeast
B_2	bean and seed sprouts, milk, cereals (wholemeal), meat, fish
B_6	cabbage, leeks, peppers (capsicum), soy beans, bananas, cereals/grains (wholemeal), potatoes, nuts, meat, fish
B_{12}	meat, vegetables containing lactic acid, milk, sour milk products, eggs, fish
Niacin	potatoes, mushrooms, pulses, peas, cereals/grains (wholemeal), meat, fish
Folic acid	vegetables (spinach, asparagus, fennel, beetroot), potatoes, orange juice, cereals/grains (wholemeal), milk
Pantothen-ic acid	broccoli, mushrooms, melon, egg yolk, cereals/grain (wholemeal), yeast, liver, meat, milk, mushrooms
Biotin (vit. H)	carrots, peas, sprouts, spinach, soy, eggs, yeast, nuts, oats, milk, cereals/grain (wholemeal), pulses, mushrooms
C	fruit (citrus fruits, berries, kiwis), vegetables (peppers/capsicum, cabbage, spinach), potatoes

NEEDED FOR	SIGNS OF A DEFICIENCY	VITAMIN
Eyes, skin, hair, cell protection, resistance to infection, protects against cancer	Poor night vision, flaky skin, poor resistance to infection	A
Bones and skin (created in the skin; obtained from the sun)	Growth problems, decalcification of bones	D
Cell protection, antioxidant, helps detoxify the liver, protects against cancer	Possibly anaemia, paleness, muscular weakness	E
Blood coagulation	Blood slow to coagulate	K
Releases energy from carbohydrate. Aids the nervous system (anti-stress vitamin), heart, muscles, memory	Tiredness, loss of appetite, muscular, circulatory and coronary weakness, cramps, poor performance	B_1
Needed for converting proteins, fats and carbohydrates into energy; also for growth and resistance to infection	Cracks on lips and at corners of mouth, dry skin, poor vitality	B_2
Important in protein metabolism; also for growth, skin, hair, nerves, production of red blood cells	Tiredness, anaemia, skin changes, loss of appetite	B_6
Cell construction and protection, resistance, production of red blood cells, tissue, growth	Anaemia, tiredness, poor resistance to infections	B_{12}
Vital for energy release in tissues and cells; for skin, heart, nerves, growth	Nausea, diarrhoea, depression	Niacin
Essential for growth and production of cells, particularly red blood cells; protects against heart attacks	Anaemia, tiredness, poor resistance to infections	Folic acid
Vital in the release of energy from foods; for bones, skin and hair, hormone production	Skin damage, dull hair, nervousness, poor resistance to infections	Pantothenic acid
Involved in the metabolism of carbohydrates, proteins, and fats; also for the blood, nerves, skin, and hair	Tiredness, loss of appetite, loss of hair, skin changes	Biotin (vit. H)
Immune system, iron absorption, connective tissue and skin cell maintenance and construction	Poor resistance to infection, tiredness, wounds slow to heal, growth problems, poor performance	C

Seven-day
highly nutritious low calorie meals
Plan

SLIM & FIT

Are you feeling listless, weak, and tired? Would you like to lose a few pounds? Just follow the menu suggestions given in our Seven-day Powerfoods Plan, and you won't have to wait long to see the results!

THE PLAN

We suggest a lunchtime and evening meal for each day of the week, which you can follow as given or switch around to suit yourself. For the best start to your day, make yourself a delicious muesli consisting of wholemeal flakes or coarsely ground cereal, fresh fruit, and low-fat quark or yoghurt after your shower. Those of us with a sweet tooth may add a little honey or apple syrup. Or, if you don't like muesli, spread some low-fat quark on a slice of wholemeal bread and top with a slice of low-fat cheese. You can eat as much fresh fruit and vegetables as you like between meals. Quench your thirst with fruit and herbal teas, and mineral water with fruit juice for extra vitamins and flavour.

FOR THE WORKERS

If you are unable to cook two meals a day, choose a recipe and prepare it in the evening. Take fresh fruit and yoghurt or quark (low-fat and low sugar if you can't manage sugar-free) for your lunch break. You could also take instant vegetable bouillon from a health food store and add boiling water for a warming soup. Any between-meal pangs of hunger can be soothed with an apple, some raw vegetables, or occasionally a wholemeal roll or a couple of biscuits. Select your own low-calorie, high-vitamin snacks.

THE WEEK'S MEALS

Monday

* ❋ Breakfast of muesli with fresh fruit, or wholemeal bread
* ❋ Vegetable and Herb Salad with apple cider dressing and a wholemeal roll
* ❋ Light Tortilla with pepper and leek ❋ Pineapple and Date Salad

Tuesday

* ❋ Breakfast of wholemeal bread, accompanied by Blueberry and Banana milk
* ❋ Curried Ginger Vegetables, accompanied by brown rice
* ❋ Cauliflower and Broccoli Salad with nutmeg mousse

Wednesday

* ❋ Breakfast of muesli with fresh fruit, or wholemeal bread
* ❋ Indonesian Vegetable Soup ❋ Iced Pineapple and Almond Shake
* ❋ Raw fruit and carrot ❋ Stove-top Spelt Cakes with Radishes

Thursday

* ❋ Breakfast of wholemeal bread, accompanied by a Raspberry and Strawberry shake
* ❋ Spinach Salad with Oranges, accompanied by wholemeal baguette
* ❋ Turnip and Turkey Fricassee with brown rice

Friday

* ❋ Breakfast of muesli with fresh fruit, or wholemeal bread
* ❋ Stir-fried Thai Vegetables with rice noodles
* ❋ Courgette and Tomato Salad, accompanied by rye baguette ❋ Tea Jelly with Grapes

Saturday

* ❋ Breakfast of wholemeal bread with Carrot and Tomato yoghurt
* ❋ Exotic Sprout Salad, accompanied by wholemeal bread or bread roll
* ❋ Linguine with Raw Tomato Sauce ❋ Citrus Fruit Platter

Sunday

* ❋ Breakfast of fruit salad with a wholemeal roll, low-fat cheese and an egg
* ❋ Raw Asparagus Salad with piquant tomato vinaigrette ❋ Strawberry and Kiwi Salad
* ❋ Light Minestrone with wholemeal bread or bread roll

Spinach

and toasted

Salad with

pine nuts

Oranges

SERVES 2: • 2 ORANGES • 70 g (3OZ) FRESH SPINACH • 1 RED ONION • 1-2 TBSP RED WINE VINEGAR • SALT • BLACK PEPPER • 3 TBSP OLIVE OIL • 1 TBSP PINE NUTS (TOASTED)

Peel the oranges and cut into segments. Wash and pick over the spinach, discarding any coarse stalks. Peel and halve the onion and slice thinly.

Combine the vinegar, salt, pepper, and oil. Stir the oranges, spinach, and onion in the dressing. Sprinkle with the toasted pine nuts.

power

PER PORTION: 195 kcal • 3 g protein • 14 g fat • 16 g carbohydrate

Exotic
with cashew nuts and ginger
Sprout Salad

Roughly chop the cashew nuts and toast until golden in a dry nonstick pan. Remove from the pan and set aside.

SERVES 2:

2 TBSP CASHEW NUTS

20G (3/4OZ) FRESH GINGER

30G (1OZ) SHALLOTS

2 TBSP SHERRY VINEGAR

SALT

WHITE PEPPER

3 TBSP THISTLE OIL

1 TBSP SESAME OIL

1 SMALL CARROT

1/2 SMALL RADISH

60G (2OZ) CUCUMBER

100G (31/2OZ) BEAN OR SEED SPROUTS

Peel and finely chop the ginger and shallots. Combine both with the vinegar, salt, and pepper, then add the two oils and beat well. Season to taste. Trim and peel the carrot, radish and cucumber and grate coarsely. Rinse the sprouts in a sieve, drain well, and pull to pieces. Combine with the grated vegetables, mix with the dressing and arrange on two plates. Sprinkle with the toasted cashew nuts and serve immediately.

NOTE: If thistle oil is unavailable, substitute sunflower oil.

Bean and seed sprouts

Set up your own little sprout farm on the windowsill so you have a constant supply of fresh vitamins. Fresh sprouts are full of beta carotene, vitamins E and K, and various B complex vitamins – including the rarely found B_{12}.

PER PORTION:

244 kcal

4 g protein

22 g fat

9 g carbohydrate

power

Cauliflower and Broccoli Salad

with nutmeg mousse

Toast the flaked almonds in a dry pan until brown, then remove. Trim and wash the cauliflower and broccoli and cut into bite-sized florets. Peel and chop the broccoli stalks. Place the vegetables in a steamer insert. Bring the stock to the boil in a saucepan. Place the steamer inside, cover with a tightly fitting lid and steam the vegetables over a low heat for 5 minutes. In a bowl, beat together the egg yolk, lemon juice, nutmeg, salt, and pepper. Place the bowl over a pot of lightly boiling water and stir the ingredients. Gradually add the hot stock, stirring constantly, until you have a fairly thick sauce. Set the bowl aside. Wash, dry and chop the parsley and add to the sauce. Season the sauce and pour over the cauliflower and broccoli. Sprinkle with the flaked almonds and serve immediately.

SERVES 2:

1 TBSP FLAKED ALMONDS

250G (9OZ) CAULIFLOWER

200G (7OZ) BROCCOLI

100ML (31/2FL OZ) VEGETABLE STOCK

1 SMALL EGG YOLK

1-2 TSP LEMON JUICE

FRESHLY GROUND NUTMEG

SALT

BLACK PEPPER

1 SPRIG PARSLEY

Vegetable stock

You can easily make your own fresh stock using onions, mushrooms, carrots, celery, tomatoes, seasoning and herbs

Dry-fry chopped onions and mushrooms until they turn dark. Chop the other vegetables and bring to the boil in about 1litre (13/4 pints) of water with the seasonings. Simmer for one hour and leave to cool. Sieve.

PER PORTION: 189 kcal• 11 g protein • 10 g fat • 17 g carbohydrate

Courgette and
with stuffed courgette flowers
Tomato Salad

Preheat the oven to 180°C/350°F. Shake the courgette flowers, then gently pull the pistil from the centre. Peel and finely chop 1 shallot. Peel and grate the carrot. Heat the oil in a small nonstick frying pan and gently cook the chopped shallot and grated carrot over a low heat for a few minutes. In a bowl, combine the Ricotta and the carrot and shallot mix, and add a little salt and pepper. Using a teaspoon, carefully place the mixture in the courgette flowers and fold the petals over the filling. Place the flowers in a gratin dish and bake in the centre of the oven for about 10 minutes, turning once halfway through.

Meanwhile, to make the dressing, peel and chop the remaining shallots and mix with the salt, pepper, mustard, and vinegar, then beat in the oil. Season to taste.

Wash and trim the courgettes. Wash the tomatoes and remove the stalk ends. Cut the tomatoes and the courgettes into thin slices and arrange on two plates. Pour over the dressing, place the stuffed courgette flowers on top, and serve the salad immediately.

Ingredients

2 COURGETTE (ZUCCHINI) FLOWERS
(WITH BABY COURGETTES ATTACHED)
3 SMALL SHALLOTS
1 SMALL CARROT
1 TSP OLIVE OIL
70G (3OZ) RICOTTA
SALT
BLACK PEPPER
1/2 TSP MUSTARD
1 TBSP WHITE WINE VINEGAR
2-3 TBSP COLD-PRESSED OLIVE OIL
150G (5OZ) SMALL COURGETTES
(ZUCCHINI)
3 SMALL, FIRM TOMATOES

power

PER PORTION: 225 kcal• 7 g protein • 18 g fat• 9 g carbohydrate

Vegetable and
with cider vinegar dressing
Herb Salad

Combine the cider vinegar with the salt and pepper, then add both oils and beat thoroughly. Season well.

SERVES 2:
2 TBSP CIDER VINEGAR
SALT
WHITE PEPPER
2 TBSP COLD-PRESSED OIL
1 TBSP WALNUT OIL
1 SMALL KOHLRABI
10 RADISHES
100G (3 1/2 OZ) NEW CARROTS
75G (3OZ) CUCUMBER
2 SPRING ONIONS
1 TBSP WALNUT HALVES
1/2 BUNCH FLAT-LEAFED PARSLEY
1/2 BUNCH OF BASIL

Peel the kohlrabi and trim and wash the radishes. Put some of the tender leaves to one side. Trim, wash and peel the carrots. Wash or peel the cucumber. Cut everything into 5mm-1 cm (1/4 - 1/2in) dice, or slice thinly.

Trim, wash and finely slice the spring onions. Chop the walnut halves. Wash, shake and chop the retained vegetable leaves, parsley and basil.

Carefully stir the prepared ingredients in the dressing and season the salad again with salt and pepper.

Getting ahead of yourself
You can prepare the salad 1 or 2 hours ahead of time and leave it to stand. Important: Cover the bowl well with clingfilm and place in the refrigerator until serving to avoid vitamin loss.

PER PORTION:
271 kcal
11 g protein
14 g fat
26 g carbohydrate

power

Coleslaw with
high in folic acid
Red Onions

Peel and finely chop the onion and combine with the vinegars, salt, and pepper. Wash the cress, thyme, and marjoram. Cut the cress and strip the stalks of the thyme and the marjoram. Add the herbs to the vinegar marinade, then add the two oils and beat well.

Trim, wash and coarsely grate the cabbage. Either use it raw, or blanch in a little salted boiling water for 3-4 minutes. Drain well, then add to the marinade. Stir well and leave to stand for about 30 minutes.

Wash and dry the pear. Cut it into quarters and remove the core. Slice the quarters widthwise and turn in the lemon juice. Arrange on the coleslaw and serve.

NOTE: If pumpkin seed oil is unavailable, substitute sunflower oil.

SERVES 2:

1 RED ONION

1 TBSP CIDER VINEGAR

1 TBSP WHITE WINE VINEGAR

SALT

BLACK PEPPER

1/2 PUNNET CRESS

1-2 SPRIGS THYME

1/2 -1 TBSP MARJORAM LEAVES

2 TBSP SUNFLOWER OIL

1 TBSP PUMPKIN SEED OIL

300G (10OZ) WHITE CABBAGE

1 PEAR

1 TBSP LEMON JUICE

Green cabbage

Like white cabbage, its somewhat coarser big brother, green cabbage is a good source of folic acid, which is so beneficial just before and during the early stages of pregnancy. However, it also contains other B vitamins and carotene. Eat raw for maximum benefit.

PER PORTION:

246 kcal

4 g protein

13 g fat

30 g carbohydrate

Raw
with piquant tomato vinaigrette
Asparagus Salad

Wash the tomato and remove the stalk. Cut into eight, remove the seeds and finely dice. Wash the chives briefly, dry thoroughly and cut into thin slices.

Mix the apple syrup with the cider vinegar, salt, and pepper. Add the two oils and beat thoroughly. Add the tomato and chives and stir carefully.

Wash and trim the asparagus and peel the lower third. Cut diagonally into very thin slices and immediately dip in the dressing. Arrange on plates.

Wash and shake dry the basil and pull the leaves from the stalks. Roughly chop the pistachio nuts. Sprinkle the basil leaves and the pistachio nuts over the salad and serve immediately.

NOTE: If pistachio oil is unavailable, substitute sunflower oil.

SERVES 2:

1 FIRM TOMATO

1/2 BUNCH OF CHIVES

2 TBSP APPLE SYRUP

1 TBSP CIDER VINEGAR

SALT

WHITE PEPPER

1 1/2 TBSP NEUTRAL OIL

2 TBSP PISTACHIO OIL

300G (10OZ) GREEN ASPARAGUS

SMALL-LEAFED BASIL

2 TBSP PISTACHIO NUTS

Asparagus

This elegant vegetable is very low in calories – only about 54 calories to 300g (10oz) – and very high in vitamins A, C, B_1, and B_2. The presence of minerals such as calcium, phosphorous, potassium, and iodine add to the value of this healthy food. Aspartic acid stimulates renal activity and is diuretic. Incidentally: green asparagus contains more vitamins than white.

PER PORTION:

248 kcal

4 g protein

23 g fat

6 g carbohydrates

Fruity
with grapefruit and apple syrup
Raw Carrots

SERVES 2: • 1 GRAPEFRUIT • 2 TBSP PUMPKIN SEED OIL • 1 TBSP CIDER VINEGAR • 2 TSP APPLE SYRUP • SALT • BLACK PEPPER • 200G (7OZ) CARROTS • 2 TBSP PUMPKIN SEEDS

Carefully peel the grapefruit and cut into segments, saving as much juice as possible. Combine the juice with the oil, vinegar, and apple syrup and stir until smooth. Season with salt and pepper. Peel, trim and coarsely grate the carrots. Stir in the dressing and arrange on plates with the grapefruit segments. Sprinkle over the pumpkin seeds.

PER PORTION: 196 kcal • 6 g protein • 14 g fat • 13 g carbohydrate

Beetroot
Winter power source
Salad

SERVES 2: • 4 SMALL BEETROOT • 1/2 BUNCH FLAT-LEAFED PARSLEY • 1 TSP MUSTARD • 1 1/2 TBSP WHITE WINE VINEGAR • SALT • BLACK PEPPER • 3 TBSP OLIVE OIL • 2 TBSP FLAKED ALMONDS (TOASTED)

Wash and scrub the beetroot thoroughly. Place unpeeled in boiling water and cook for about 30 minutes. Wash and shake dry the parsley and chop. Mix with the mustard, vinegar, salt, and pepper and add the oil. Peel the beetroot, cut into slices and then into thick strips. Stir in the dressing and sprinkle with almonds before serving.

PER PORTION: 190 kcal • 3 g protein • 16 g fat • 9 g carbohydrate

Beetroot Salad

with horseradish for extra bite

with Pears

Wash and trim the Brussels sprouts. Remove most of the leaves and cut a cross into the base of the stalks.

Bring the stock to the boil in a saucepan. Place the Brussels sprouts in a steamer insert and place in the saucepan. Cover with a tightly fitting lid and steam for about 5 minutes. Add the Brussels sprout leaves and steam together for another 1-2 minutes.

Peel and core the pear and coarsely grate the flesh. Place in a dish and immediately add the lemon juice, crème fraîche, and some of the vegetable stock. Whip the cream until stiff and gently fold into the dressing. Season with horseradish, salt, and pepper. Cut the roast beef into thick strips, arrange with the Brussels sprouts and pour over the dressing.

SERVES 2:

250G (9OZ) BABY BRUSSELS SPROUTS

100ML (31/2FL OZ) VEGETABLE STOCK (FROM A CARTON OR JAR)

1 SMALL PEAR

1 TBSP LEMON JUICE

2 TBSP CRÈME FRAÎCHE

40ML (11/2FL OZ) WHIPPING CREAM

2 TSP GRATED HORSERADISH

BLACK PEPPER

50G (13/4OZ) THINLY SLICED ROAST BEEF

PER PORTION: 252 kcal • 11 g protein • 14 g fat • 24 g carbohydrate

Vegetable Vitamins

with radish vinaigrette

Wash and peel the carrots, horseradish, and courgette (zucchini). Grate coarsely or cut into thin slices. Wash the tomato and cut into slices (without the stalk base).

SERVES 2:
100G (3½ OZ) CARROTS
1 SMALL PIECE OF HORSERADISH
1 SMALL COURGETTE (ZUCCHINI)
1 TOMATO
1 SPRING ONION
6 RADISHES
1 TBSP LEMON JUICE
2 TSP APPLE SYRUP
1½ TBSP CIDER VINEGAR
2 TBSP SUNFLOWER OIL
2 TBSP OLIVE OIL
SALT
BLACK PEPPER
1 TBSP SUNFLOWER SEEDS

Wash, trim and thinly slice the spring onion.

Wash and trim the radishes. Chop a small amount of the tender leaves, slice half the radishes, and coarsely grate the rest.

Combine the chopped radish leaves with the lemon juice, apple syrup, and cider vinegar, and add the two oils. Stir in the grated radishes, then season the dressing with salt and pepper.

Arrange the remaining ingredients on a serving dish or two individual plates. Pour over the radish vinaigrette and sprinkle with the sunflower seeds.

Radishes and horseradish

These "cousins" contain a generous amount of vitamin C as well as several other essential vitamins and minerals. Because they are usually eaten raw, you get the maximum benefit from the nutrients.

PER PORTION:

300 kcal

9 g protein

19 g fat

23 g carbohydrate

power

the classic Italian soup

Light
Minestrone

Wash, peel and dice the potatoes. Wash, trim and chop the leek, courgettes, carrots, and fennel.

Wash the tomato and carefully slit the ends. Place in boiling water for a few moments, then skin and chop roughly, discarding the core. Peel and finely chop the onion.

Heat the oil and sauté the chopped onion until translucent. Add the fennel, carrots, leek, and courgettes and cook gently. Pour over the stock. Add the tomatoes and the potatoes. Cover with a tightly fitting lid and cook over a medium heat for about 20 minutes.

Wash and shake dry the herbs. Remove the leaves from the coarse stalks and chop. Add to the soup and season with salt and black pepper. Sprinkle with grated Pecorino before serving.

SERVES 2:

150G (5OZ) FIRM POTATOES

1 YOUNG LEEK

100G (3½ OZ) COURGETTES (ZUCCHINI)

100G (3½ OZ) CARROTS

½ HEAD OF FENNEL

200G (7OZ) TOMATOES

1 SMALL ONION

1 TBSP OLIVE OIL

500ML (18FL OZ) HOT VEGETABLE STOCK

½ BUNCH OF FLAT-LEAFED PARSLEY

½ BUNCH OF BASIL

SALT

BLACK PEPPER

30G (1OZ) PIECE OF PECORINO CHEESE

power

PER PORTION: 394 kcal • 17 g protein • 13 g fat • 54 g carbohydrate

Cold

refreshing and full of vitamins

Vegetable Soup

Gently slit the round ends of the tomatoes. Place in boiling water for a few moments, then remove with a slotted spoon. Skin, remove the core and stalk, then chop.

SERVES 2:
250G (9OZ) AROMATIC TOMATOES
1 SMALL SPANISH ONION
1/2 CUCUMBER
1 SMALL GREEN PEPPER (CAPSICUM)
2 CLOVES GARLIC
1/2 - 1 TBSP RED WINE VINEGAR
1 SLICE OF WHITE BREAD
2 TBSP COLD-PRESSED OLIVE OIL
SALT
BLACK PEPPER

Peel the onion and the cucumber. Halve, trim and wash the pepper. Finely dice the vegetables. Peel the garlic and blend to a puree with the tomatoes and a generous half of the other vegetables.

Sprinkle the vinegar and about 100ml (3 1/2 fl oz) water over the bread and leave for a few minutes to absorb. Add to the pureed vegetables with the oil, and puree until smooth. Season with salt and pepper and cover with clingfilm. Place in the refrigerator to chill for about 30 minutes. Cover the remaining vegetables and place in the refrigerator to chill.

Stir the soup and season. Add the remaining vegetables and serve immediately.

Refreshing sources of vitamins

Cold soups are very refreshing on a hot summer's day, and also provide generous amounts of vitamins. The vegetables are processed raw, which means that most of the vitamins are retained. It is important to cover and chill the soup to let the flavours develop.

PER PORTION:

187 kcal

5 g protein

9 g fat

23 g carbohydrate

power

Indonesian
with celery and bean sprouts
Vegetable Soup

Pour a generous amount of hot water over the noodles in a dish and leave to stand.

Bring 500ml (18fl oz) water to the boil. Wash the drumsticks and place in the water. Wash the lemon under hot water and peel. Peel and finely chop the ginger. Place both in the water with the chicken, bay leaf and peanuts. Cover and simmer over a low heat for about 30 minutes.

Rinse the beansprouts under cold water and leave to drain. Wash and trim the celery and the spring onions. Wash and peel the carrots. Cut everything into thin slices.

Remove the drumsticks from the stock. Discard the skin and bones and cut the meat into thin slices. Strain the stock and heat through again. Season with soy sauce, pepper and lemon juice. Place the chicken, drained noodles, and the prepared vegetables in the stock and cook for 3-4 minutes. Sprinkle with the coriander leaves and serve.

SERVES 2:

- 20G (3/4 OZ) GLASS NOODLES
- 4-5 CHICKEN DRUMSTICKS
- 1 SMALL UNWAXED LEMON (JUICE AND RIND)
- 15G (1/2 OZ) FRESH GINGER
- 1 BAY LEAF
- 1 TBSP TOASTED PEANUTS
- 75G (3OZ) BEANSPROUTS
- 2 STICKS CELERY
- 2 SPRING ONIONS
- 1 CARROT
- 2-3 TBSP LIGHT SOY SAUCE
- WHITE PEPPER
- HANDFUL OF FRESH CORIANDER LEAVES

PER PORTION: 567 kcal• 53 g protein • 30 g fat• 23 g carbohydrate

Cream of
full of vitamin C and fibre
Radish Soup

Thoroughly wash the radishes and leaves. Put some of the tender leaves and 2-3 radishes aside. Roughly chop the remainder. Peel and finely dice the shallot. Wash, peel and roughly chop the potatoes.

Heat the oil in a saucepan, add the shallots and cook until translucent. Sweat the chopped radishes, the radish leaves, and the potatoes, then pour over the stock. Cover with a tightly fitting lid and simmer gently over a medium heat for about 20 minutes. Puree the soup in a blender until smooth and reheat. Add 1 tbsp crème fraîche and season with salt and pepper.

Thinly slice the retained radishes and radish leaves.

Pour the soup into two bowls and spoon a little crème fraîche into the centre. Sprinkle with the radish slices and leaves.

SERVES 2:
1 LARGE BUNCH OF RADISHES
1 SHALLOT
125G (4OZ) FLOURY POTATOES
2 TBSP SUNFLOWER OIL
300ML (10FL OZ) VEGETABLE STOCK
2 TBSP CRÈME FRAÎCHE
SALT
WHITE PEPPER

PER PORTION: 153 kcal• 2 g protein• 9 g fat • 14 g carbohydrate

Swede Stew with Steak

with lots of carotene and vitamin C

Tartare Dumplings

Combine the steak tartare with the egg, breadcrumbs, salt, pepper, and cayenne pepper and season well. Shape into small dumplings.

SERVES 2:

175G (6OZ) STEAK TARTARE

1 SMALL EGG

2-3 TBSP BREADCRUMBS

SALT

BLACK PEPPER

CAYENNE PEPPER

400G (14OZ) SWEDE

1 LEEK

400ML (14FL OZ) VEGETABLE STOCK

1-2 TSP OIL

1/2 BUNCH OF BASIL

1/2 -1 TSP CURRY POWDER

1/2 TSP CUMIN

Trim and peel the swede. Cut into thin slices, then into thin strips. Trim the leek, slice lengthwise and wash thoroughly. Shake dry and cut into thin slices. Bring the stock to the boil. Place the swede and the leek in the stock, cover with a tightly fitting lid and simmer gently over a low heat for about 10 minutes. Meanwhile, heat the oil in a small nonstick frying pan. Brown the steak tartare dumplings on all sides over a low heat for about 10 minutes.

Wash and shake dry the basil, keeping some of the leaves for garnishing. Finely chop the remaining leaves and add to the vegetables. Season with curry, cumin, salt, and pepper. Add the steak tartare dumplings and garnish with the basil.

Swedes

They contain generous amounts of vitamins and minerals, and are especially high in carotene, niacin, vitamin B$_6$, and vitamin C.

PER PORTION:

464 kcal

35 g protein

17 g fat

44 g carbohydrate

power

Sauerkraut Soup
tasty and high in vitamin C
with Chive Cream

SERVES 2: • 1 SMALL ONION • 1 SMALL FLOURY POTATO • 1 TBSP BUTTER • 150G (5OZ) SAUERKRAUT • 400ML (14FL OZ)

VEGETABLE STOCK • SALT • BLACK PEPPER • 1 BUNCH OF CHIVES • 50ML (13/4 FL OZ) SOUR CREAM

Peel and finely dice the onion and the potato, and sweat in the butter in a saucepan. Add the

sauerkraut and the stock, cover, and simmer gently for about 10 minutes. Puree and season.

Wash and slice the chives and combine with the sour cream, salt, and pepper. Pour over the

soup before serving.

PER PORTION: 253 kcal • 7 g protein • 11 g fat • 33 g carbohydrate

Creamy
with toasted almonds
Leek Soup

SERVES 2: • 1 LEEK • 100G (31/2 OZ) FLOURY POTATOES • 250ML (8FL OZ) VEGETABLE STOCK • SALT • WHITE PEPPER • 1

TSP FRESH THYME • 50G (13/4 FL OZ) FULL-FAT YOGHURT • 2 TBSP FLAKED ALMONDS (TOASTED)

Slit the leek in half lengthwise, wash and trim, and cut into slices. Peel, wash and finely chop

the potatoes. Place both in a saucepan with the stock, cover with a lid and simmer gently for 15

minutes. Puree the soup and season with salt, pepper, and thyme. Add the yoghurt and garnish

with the almonds.

PER PORTION: 187 kcal • 8 g protein • 7 g fat • 24 g carbohydrate

Curried Ginger
with chili and coconut milk
Vegetables

Slit open the chili, trim, wash and cut into thin rings. Peel and finely chop the garlic and ginger. Wash, trim and slice the spring onions.

Wash and trim the mangetout and cut each one into three diagonally. Wash and peel the carrots. Cut into thin strips lengthwise, then slice as thinly as possible. Rinse the beansprouts in a sieve under cold water and drain well.

Heat the oil in a wok. Add the garlic, ginger, and chili rings and stir-fry lightly. Add the mangetout and carrots and stir-fry for 2-3 minutes. Then add the spring onions and cook for a little longer. Add the coconut milk, curry paste, and soy sauce and heat through. Add the beansprouts and heat for a further 1-2 minutes. Wash and roughly chop a few coriander leaves. Sprinkle over the vegetables and serve immediately.

SERVES 2:

1 RED CHILI

1 CLOVE GARLIC

20G (3/4 OZ) FRESH GINGER

1/2 BUNCH OF SPRING ONIONS

100G (31/2 OZ) MANGETOUT

150G (5OZ) CARROTS

70G (3OZ) FRESH BEANSPROUTS

1 TBSP OIL

200ML (7FL OZ) UNSWEETENED COCONUT MILK

1-2 TSP HOT CURRY PASTE

3 TBSP LIGHT SOY SAUCE

SALT

FRESH CORIANDER LEAVES

power

PER PORTION: 234 kcal• 6 g protein • 16 g fat • 19 g carbohydrate

Stir-fried Pumpkin
with curry, chili and grapes
and Brown Rice

Gently heat 1/2 tbsp olive oil. Add the rice and stir, then pour over the stock and cover with a tightly fitting lid. Cook over a low heat until just firm to the bite (20-40 minutes, depending on the type; refer to packet instructions).

SERVES 2:
1½ TBSP COLD-PRESSED OLIVE OIL
100G (3½ OZ) BROWN RICE
250ML (8FL OZ) VEGETABLE STOCK
500G (1LB 2OZ) PUMPKIN
SALT
1/2 BUNCH OF SPRING ONIONS
1-2 SMALL RED CHILI PEPPERS
1 SMALL CLOVE GARLIC
50G (SCANT 2OZ) GRAPES
1/4-1/2 TBSP CURRY POWDER
BLACK PEPPER
2-3 TBSP PUMPKIN SEEDS

Peel the pumpkin and remove the seeds and tough fibres. Cut the flesh into 1-2 cm (1/2 -3/4 in) pieces. Bring 100ml (3½ fl oz) lightly salted water to the boil. Place the pumpkin in the boiling water, cover with a tightly fitting lid and cook for about 5 minutes. Drain, saving the liquid.

Wash and trim the spring onions and cut into thin rings diagonally. Trim, de-seed and wash the chilies, then finely chop. Peel the garlic, and finely chop. Rinse the grapes under hot water.

Heat the remaining oil in a large frying pan. Add the chopped chili and garlic to the oil and stir-fry gently for about 2 minutes.

Stir in the curry powder and the pumpkin liquid. Add the grapes and the pumpkin to the pan. Season with salt and pepper and cover. Cook over a low heat for another 5 minutes. Drain the rice and add to the pan. Combine all the ingredients, season, and sprinkle with the pumpkin seeds before serving.

PER PORTION: 519 kcal • 18 g protein• 19 g fat • 74 g carbohydrate

Light
with pepper and leek
Tortilla

Wash the potatoes and cook unpeeled in a little water with salt and the cumin for about 20 minutes. Drain, cool slightly and peel. Cut into thick slices.

Wash the courgette, cut in half lengthwise and slice. Halve, trim and wash the pepper and chop. Trim the leek, slit lengthwise and clean. Shake dry and cut into thin rings.

Heat the oil in a large nonstick frying pan. Fry the potatoes in the oil until golden brown. Add the courgette slices, the chopped pepper, and sliced leek and cook over a low heat for about 5 minutes, stirring gently.

SERVES 2:
200G (7OZ) FIRM POTATOES
SALT
1 TBSP CUMIN
1 SMALL COURGETTE (ZUCCHINI)
1 RED PEPPER (CAPSICUM)
1 YOUNG LEEK
1½ TBSP OLIVE OIL
1 CHILI PEPPER
1 SMALL CLOVE GARLIC
4 EGGS
BLACK PEPPER

Slit open the chili pepper, remove the seeds and finely chop the flesh. Peel and chop the garlic. Beat the chili and garlic with the eggs and season with salt and pepper. Pour the egg mix over the potatoes and vegetables. Cover with a lid and set over a very low heat for about 5 minutes.

PER PORTION: 474 kcal• 31 gprotein • 30 g fat • 20 g carbohydrate

a light classic

Provençal
Peppers

Soak a clay pot and lid in water for 15-30 minutes. Meanwhile, halve, seed and core the peppers. Wash the halves and cut into strips.

SERVES 2:

1 SMALL RED, YELLOW, AND GREEN PEPPER (CAPSICUM)

400G (14OZ) BEEFSTEAK TOMATOES

125G (4OZ) COURGETTES (ZUCCHINI)

125G (4OZ) ONIONS

1 CLOVE GARLIC

2 SPRIGS ROSEMARY

3-4 SPRIGS THYME

SALT

BLACK PEPPER

2 TSP LEMON JUICE

1 TBSP OLIVE OIL

100ML (3 1/2 FL OZ) VEGETABLE STOCK

Slit the tops of the tomatoes and place in boiling water for a few seconds. Remove with a slotted spoon, then skin them, remove the core and chop roughly. Wash, trim and roughly chop the courgettes. Peel and finely chop the onions and garlic. Wash and shake dry the herbs, putting some to one side for garnish. Finely chop the rest.

Place the vegetables in the clay pot together with the salt, pepper, lemon juice, oil, and stock. Cover with the lid and place in the bottom of a cold oven. Bake at 200°C (400°F) for about 1 hour. Stir the vegetables, season, and sprinkle with the herbs before serving.

Gentle cooking in a clay pot

Cooking in a clay pot is the perfect way to cook vegetables. Although they take somewhat longer than when cooked in a saucepan, the vegetables steam gently in their own juices in a firmly sealed pot, and this also helps to retain the nutrients. A minimum of fat is used, and the vegetables are wonderfully light and aromatic.

PER PORTION:

175 kcal

6 g protein

6 g fat

24 g carbohydrate

Salsify and

with plenty of vitamins B₁ and E

Ham Ragout

Thoroughly wash and scrape the salsify. Bring plenty of boiling water to the boil in a wide pot and add the salt and vinegar. Boil the salsify for about 15-20 minutes, taking care not to let it become too soft.

SERVES 2:
500G (1LB 2OZ) SALSIFY
SALT
2 TBSP VINEGAR
1 SMALL ONION
1 TBSP BUTTER
1½ TBSP FLOUR
125ML (4FL OZ) VEGETABLE STOCK
125ML (4FL OZ) MILK
WHITE PEPPER
100G (3½ OZ) SMOKED HAM (1 THICK SLICE)
½ BUNCH OF BASIL

Drain the salsify and rinse under cold water. Either pull off or peel the dark skin and cut the salsify into 3-4 cm (1¼-1½ in) lengths (wear rubber gloves).

Peel and finely chop the onion. Melt the butter in a saucepan and cook the onion until translucent. Sprinkle over the flour and, stirring continuously, cook until golden. Gradually add the stock and the milk. Cook until slightly thickened, then season well with salt and pepper. Dice the ham; wash and finely chop the basil. Add both to the sauce with the salsify and heat through. Season well.

Salsify

Salsify is easy to digest and contains good amounts of vitamins, such as carotene, vitamins B₁ and E. Diabetics will be interested to learn of its high insulin level, a carbohydrate that poses no problem for them.

PER PORTION:

274 kcal

15 g protein

11 g fat

16 g carbohydrate

Stove-top Spelt Cakes

healthy and elegant

with Radishes

Gently roast the spelt in a small dry saucepan over medium heat. Pour over the stock and allow to bubble. Cover with a lid and simmer for about 10 minutes over a low heat, then remove from the heat and leave to swell for about 20 minutes.

Wash and trim the radishes. Finely chop a few of the tops, and cut the radishes into four or eight pieces. Peel and finely chop the onion. Melt 1/2 tbsp butter and gently sauté the onion until translucent. Add the radishes and tops. Season well, then cover and steam over a low heat for about 5 minutes. Do not add any more liquid.

Beat the eggs and add to the spelt. Season with salt and pepper. Melt the remaining butter in a nonstick pan. Drop small amounts of the spelt mixture into the pan and fry. Check the flavour of the radish mixture, then arrange on top of the cakes. Add a tiny dollop of crème fraîche to each.

SERVES 2:

70G (3OZ) GROUND SPELT

125ML (4FL OZ) VEGETABLE STOCK

1 LARGE BUNCH OF RADISHES WITH TOPS

1 RED ONION

1½ TBSP BUTTER

SALT

BLACK PEPPER

2 SMALL EGGS

1 TBSP CRÈME FRAÎCHE

PER PORTION: 390 kcal • 20 g protein • 18 g fat • 37 g carbohydrate

Carrot Crêpes
vitamins for gourmets
with Asparagus

To make the crêpes, combine the eggs, salt, 100ml (3½ fl oz) water, and the flour. Cover and leave to stand for about 30 minutes.

Wash, trim and peel the asparagus. Bring a little water to the boil with the salt, 2 tbsp of butter, and the sugar. Place the asparagus in a steamer inside the saucepan. Cover with a tightly fitting lid and steam the asparagus for 20-30 minutes until just cooked.

Beat together the quark, apple syrup, lemon juice, salt, and pepper, thinning slightly with a little milk. Wash the herbs, shake dry and chop, and add to the quark. Season well.

Wash, trim and peel the carrots. Grate finely and add to the crêpe mixture. Using a nonstick pan, cook two pancakes in succession, melting about 1 tsp butter in the pan for each one. Drain the asparagus. Divide into two equal portions and wrap a pancake around each portion. Place on a plate and serve with the herby quark.

SERVES 2:

2 EGGS

SALT

50G (1¾ OZ) WHEAT FLOUR

750G (1LB 10OZ) WHITE ASPARAGUS

4 TBSP BUTTER

1 TSP SUGAR

125G (4OZ) QUARK (20% FAT)

½ TBSP APPLE SYRUP

½ TBSP LEMON JUICE

BLACK PEPPER

MILK

½ BUNCH OF MIXED HERBS

80G (SCANT 3 OZ) CARROTS

power

PER PORTION: 415 kcal • 28 g protein • 17 g fat • 30 g carbohydrate

Turnip and Turkey
with brown rice
Fricassee

SERVES 2:
200G (7OZ) SMALL WHITE TURNIPS
200G (7OZ) CARROTS
SALT
200G (7OZ) TURKEY BREAST
1/2 BUNCH OF BASIL
1 TBSP BUTTER
1½ TBSP FLOUR
125ML (4FL OZ) MILK
125ML (4FL OZ) STOCK
BLACK PEPPER
LEMON JUICE
1-2 TBSP GROUND DRIED MUSHROOMS

Wash, trim and slice the turnips and the carrots, halving any large slices. Place in a steamer insert.

Bring a little salted water to the boil in a small saucepan. Place the insert in the saucepan, cover with a tightly fitting lid and steam the vegetables for about 10 minutes until still slightly firm to the bite.

Meanwhile, rinse the turkey under cold water, dry with paper towels and cut into small pieces. Wash and shake dry the basil, putting some of the leaves aside as garnish, and finely chop the rest.

Melt the butter in a wide saucepan, add the turkey meat and fry until golden brown on all sides. Sprinkle over the flour, stir to combine, then gradually add the milk and stock. Simmer the sauce gently for 5 minutes over a low heat, stirring occasionally.

Add the prepared vegetables and the basil and return to the boil. Season the fricassee with salt, pepper, lemon juice, and the ground mushrooms. Sprinkle with the basil leaves before serving.

PER PORTION: 310 kcal• 29 g protein • 6 g fat• 21 g carbohydrate

Stir-fried

with hot chili and sweet pineapple

Thai Vegetables

Peel and finely chop the garlic and ginger. Slit open the chili and scrape out the seeds. Wash the chili and slice into thin rings. Wash and trim the broccoli and divide into florets. Peel and chop the stalks. Wash and peel the carrot and cut diagonally into thin slices. Wash and pick over the pak choi and cut into thick slices. Wash and trim the spring onion and cut diagonally into thin slices. Peel the pineapple, remove the core and dice. Heat the oil in a wok. Add the garlic, ginger, and chili rings and stir-fry briefly. Add the broccoli and carrots and stir-fry for about 2 minutes. Add the spring onion and cook for 1 minute. Sprinkle the sugar over the vegetables and pour over the stock. Add the pak choi, pineapple, fish sauce and a squeeze of lime juice and bring to the boil. Serve garnished with coriander leaves.

SERVES 2:

1 CLOVE GARLIC

15G (1/2 OZ) FRESH GINGER

1 RED CHILI PEPPER

200G (7OZ) BROCCOLI

1 CARROT

75G (21/2 OZ) PAK CHOI

2 SPRING ONIONS

2-3 SLICES FRESH PINEAPPLE

1 TBSP OIL

2 TSP BROWN SUGAR

100ML (31/2 FL OZ) VEGETABLE STOCK

2 TBSP FISH SAUCE

LIME JUICE

FRESH CORIANDER LEAVES

PER PORTION: 235 kcal • 8 g protein • 10 g fat • 33 g carbohydrate

Linguine with Raw
aromatic and low in calories
Tomato Sauce

Slit the ends of the tomatoes and place in boiling water for a few seconds. Remove from the water, skin, and remove the core and seeds. Chop into small pieces.

SERVES 2:
400G (14OZ) RIPE TOMATOES
1 CLOVE GARLIC
2 TBSP AROMATIC COLD-PRESSED OLIVE OIL
SALT
BLACK PEPPER
200G (7OZ) LINGUINE
FRESH BASIL
2 TBSP GRATED PARMESAN

Peel and finely chop or crush the garlic. Combine with the tomato and oil, and season with salt and pepper. Cover and place on one side.

Cook the linguine in plenty of salt water in accordance with the packet instructions. Drain well in sieve.

Stir the tomato sauce and taste. Heat through briefly, then combine with the pasta and serve immediately. Wash and dry the basil and sprinkle over the pasta with the Parmesan.

Tomatoes

Most pasta sauces are cooked for long periods of time, which reduces the vitamin content. But not in this case: the tomatoes are still bursting with vitamins A, C, and E and with the B complex vitamins when you sit down to eat them. Tomatoes are also low in calories, diuretic, and good for the blood.

PER PORTION:

512 kcal

18 g protein

12 g fat

81 g carbohydrate

power

Mixed

with a refreshing yoghurt cream

Berries

Combine the yoghurt with the apple syrup, milk, and a little ground cinnamon and divide between two dessert plates.

Wash the lemon thoroughly under running hot water and dry well. Finely grate the rind and squeeze the juice. Combine both in a bowl with the vanilla sugar.

Wash, pick over and drain the raspberries, blueberries, and currants. Use a fork to strip the redcurrants and blackcurrants from the stalks. Wash and stone the plums. Cut the plums into segments. Carefully stir the fruit in the lemon juice. Arrange the berries and the plums on the yoghurt, sprinkle lightly with the cinnamon and serve soon.

SERVES 2:

100G (3½ OZ) LOW FAT YOGHURT

1 TBSP APPLE SYRUP

2 TBSP MILK

1/4 TSP GROUND CINNAMON

1/2 UNWAXED LEMON

1/2 SACHET VANILLA SUGAR

50G (SCANT 2OZ) SMALL RASPBERRIES

50G (SCANT 2OZ) BLUEBERRIES

40G (1½ OZ) REDCURRANTS

40G (1½ OZ) BLACKCURRANTS

2 YELLOW PLUMS

PER PORTION: 173 kcal • 4 g protein • 1 g fat • 38 g carbohydrate

Strawberry and

contains plenty of vitamin C

Kiwi Salad

SERVES 2: • 1/2 UNWAXED LIME • 1 TBSP MAPLE SYRUP • PINCH OF GROUND VANILLA • 250G (9OZ) SMALL STRAWBERRIES • 2 KIWIS • 1-2 TBSP PECAN NUTS (ROUGHLY CHOPPED)

Wash the lime under hot water, grate the rind and squeeze the juice. Combine the rind and the juice with the maple syrup and vanilla. Wash the strawberries briefly, remove the stalks and cut thickly. Peel and halve the kiwis and cut into slices. Arrange the fruit on plates, pour over the syrup and top with the pecan nuts.

PER PORTION: 104 Kcal • 1 g protein • 5 g fat • 15 g carbohydrate

Date and

with lime juice and honey

Pineapple Salad

SERVES 2: • 1/2 SMALL PINEAPPLE • 1 KIWI • 4 FRESH DATES • 2 TBSP LIME JUICE • 2 TSP BROWN SUGAR • 1 TBSP ACACIA HONEY • 1 TBSP DRIED COCONUT (TOASTED)

Peel the pineapple, cut into four lengthwise and remove the core. Cut into slices, saving as much of the juice as possible. Peel and halve the kiwi and slice the halves. Remove the stones from the dates and cut into segments. Stir together the lime and pineapple juices, sugar, and honey. Add the fruit to this mixture and sprinkle with the toasted coconut.

PER PORTION: 125 kcal • 1 g protein • 1 g fat • 31 g carbohydrate

Melon and Mango

refreshing and healthy

Soup with Kiwi

Halve the orange and squeeze out the juice. Halve the melon and remove the seeds and fibres. Using a melon ball, scoop several little balls out of the melon flesh, cover and place in the refrigerator. Remove the rest of the melon from the skin. Peel the mango and remove the flesh from the stone. Puree the melon and mango with the orange juice, and strain through a sieve for a really smooth soup. Flavour the soup with lemon juice and a few drops of Angostura and divide between two bowls.

Halve and peel the kiwi and cut into slices. Place in the soup, together with the melon balls. Decorate with lemon balm.

SERVES 2:

1 ORANGE, WELL CHILLED

1/2 RIPE MELON (E.G. CANTALOUPE), WELL CHILLED

1 SMALL RIPE MANGO, WELL CHILLED

1-2 TBSP LEMON JUICE

ANGOSTURA BITTERS

1 KIWI

FRESH LEMON BALM

Melons, mangoes and kiwis

They are all very low in calories and very high in vitamins, such as carotinoids and minerals. Melons are diuretic and generally cleansing, so they are an ideal part of any diet or beauty regime. Mangoes provide beta-carotene (a type of carotinoid) as well as vitamins from the B complex, and kiwis contain a generous amount of vitamin C and folic acid.

PER PORTION:

122 kcal

2 g protein

1 g fat

31 g carbohydrate

Jellied
with juicy plums
Buttermilk Soup

Soak the gelatine in a generous amount of cold water for about 5 minutes. Remove 3 leaves without wringing and dissolve in a saucepan over a low heat. Stir into the buttermilk. Dissolve the remaining leaves and combine with the apple juice.

SERVES 2:

5 LEAVES WHITE GELATINE

250ML (8FL OZ) BUTTERMILK

125ML (4FL OZ) APPLE JUICE

1/2 TSP GRATED LEMON RIND
(UNWAXED FRUIT)

2 TBSP APPLE SYRUP

1/2 TSP GROUND CINNAMON

150G (5OZ) PLUMS

1/2 SACHET VANILLA SUGAR

Combine the buttermilk with the lemon rind, apple syrup, and ground cinnamon. Pour into 2 small soup plates and chill to set. Do not chill the apple juice.

Wash, halve and stone the plums and sprinkle over the vanilla sugar. Arrange on the jellied buttermilk, perhaps cut into fan shapes. Pour over the apple juice and place in the refrigerator to set, covering the plates with clingfilm to prevent vitamin loss.

Plums

Carotene, B vitamins and vitamin C dominate these purple fruits, which also contain plenty of minerals. Optimum benefit is gained from carotene, the precursor to vitamin A, if you slice open the plums and combine them with a little fat (as in the buttermilk). Incidentally, this recipe is also delicious made with strawberries.

PER PORTION:

207 kcal

7 g protein

1 g fat

47 g carbohydrate

power

Citus Fruit

with light quark cream

Platter

Wash the lime and lemon in hot water and dry well. Finely pare some of the rind, and finely grate some of the rest. Squeeze the juice of both fruits.

SERVES 2:
1 SMALL UNWAXED LIME
1/2 UNWAXED LEMON
2 TBSP MAPLE SYRUP
125G (4OZ) QUARK (20% FAT)
1 LARGE ORANGE
1 LARGE PINK GRAPEFRUIT
30G (1OZ) PECAN NUTS
2 TSP CHOCOLATE FLAKES

Combine the juice and the grated rind with the maple syrup and quark.

Peel the orange and the grapefruit, removing all the pith. Remove the flesh segments from between the membranes.

Divide the quark cream between two plates. Arrange the orange and grapefruit segments decoratively on top. Roughly chop the pecan nuts and sprinkle over the desserts with the chocolate flakes and shredded lime and lemon rinds.

Citrus fruits

Whether grapefruit, lime, orange, or lemon – citrus fruits provide you with beta carotene and vitamin C, and contain large quantities of minerals. Because the vitamins are delicate, you should always eat citrus fruit as soon as you have peeled it. Almost as good: drink a large glass of freshly squeezed juice.

PER PORTION:

332 Kcal

10 g protein

18 g fat

37 g carbohydrate

Tea Jelly
a little light relief
with Grapes

Brew the fruit tea in a tea pot with 250ml (8fl oz) boiling water and leave to stand for 5 minutes. Soak the gelatine in plenty of cold water for 5 minutes.

Wash the lemon in hot water and dry. Finely grate the rind and squeeze the juice. Gently squeeze the gelatine and dissolve in the hot tea. Add the lemon juice and rind and 1 tbsp of the icing sugar.

Wash the grapes. Put some aside for decoration, halve the remainder and remove the seeds. Place in tall glasses and pour over the tea. Leave in the refrigerator to set.

Beat the yoghurt with the remaining icing sugar. Pour onto the tea jelly and serve decorated with grapes.

SERVES 2:

3 TBSP FRUIT TEA LEAVES

3 SHEETS WHITE GELATINE

1/2 UNWAXED LEMON

2 TBSP ICING SUGAR

75G (3OZ) EACH RED AND WHITE GRAPES

75G (3OZ) YOGHURT (1.5% FAT)

Grapes

They are full of glucose, which provides instant energy when required. Although the amount of vitamins does not quite compare with levels in other fruits, grapes are still a valuable fruit. They stimulate the metabolism and the digestive system, detoxify the body, stimulate the production of blood, and are generally beneficial to health, looks, and wellbeing.

PER PORTION:

101 kcal

4 g protein

1 g fat

22 g carbohydrate

Blueberry and Banana Milk

full of vitamin B$_6$ and folic acid

Briefly wash, then pick over the blueberries and drain well. Peel and roughly chop the banana and sprinkle over the lemon juice. Blend the blueberries with the banana and the pear syrup in a high-sided bowl. Stir in the ground vanilla and cold milk, then pour into glasses and serve immediately.

FOR 2 GLASSES:

200G (7OZ) BLUEBERRIES

1 SMALL RIPE BANANA

1 TBSP LEMON JUICE

1 TBSP PEAR SYRUP

PINCH OF GROUND VANILLA

300ML (10FL OZ) ICE COLD MILK

Blueberries and bananas

These blue woodland berries, also known as whortleberries or bilberries, contain large amounts of protective antioxidants, flavonoids and vitamin C – reason enough to treat yourself to them as often as you like. Flavonoids help strengthen capillaries and may lower the risk of heart disease. Although bananas contain more energy and less vitamin C than other fruits, they also contain certain vitamins which other fruits do not, especially B$_6$, pantothenic acid, and folic acid.

PER PORTION:

249 kcal

3 g protein

3 g fat

20 g carbohydrate

Raspberry and

berry healthy

Strawberry Shake

Wash and pick over the berries. Use a sharp knife to hull the strawberries.

FOR 2 GLASSES:
80G (3OZ) RASPBERRIES
80G (3OZ) STRAWBERRIES
2 TBSP PEAR SYRUP
PINCH OF GROUND CINNAMON
PINCH OF GROUND VANILLA
125ML (4FL OZ) CURDS
125ML (4FL OZ) MILK

Puree the berries and pass through a sieve to remove the seeds.

Add the pear syrup, cinnamon and vanilla to the fruit puree. Add the curds and milk, beating with a whisk.

Pour the shake into glasses and serve immediately.

Raspberries and strawberries

Just 125g (4oz) strawberries will give you your daily requirement of vitamin C, the most important vitamin for resistance. Its other components make this delicious fruit a popular choice for health and beauty. Important: Strawberries quickly lose their flavour and vitamins, so eat as soon as possible after picking. Raspberries are almost equally healthy (and sensitive), but do not contain quite the same levels of vitamins.

PER DRINK:

186 kcal

4 g protein

3 g fat

21 g carbohydrate

power

Fruity
best well chilled
Cucumber Drink

FOR 2 GLASSES: • 200G (7OZ) CUCUMBER (WELL CHILLED) • 2 KIWIS (WELL CHILLED) • 1/2 TSP GROUND GINGER • SALT • BLACK PEPPER • WELL-CHILLED MINERAL WATER

Peel and roughly chop the cucumber, and puree. Peel and roughly chop the kiwis. Add to the cucumber and blend again briefly. Do not process for long, as otherwise the shake will become bitter. Flavour the cucumber and kiwi puree with ground ginger, salt, and pepper and pour into tall glasses. Top with well chilled mineral water and serve immediately.

PER DRINK: 42 kcal • 1 g protein • 1 g fat • 10 g carbohydrate

Carrot and
for a healthy snack
Tomato Yoghurt

FOR 2 GLASSES: • 150G (5FL OZ) LOW-FAT YOGHURT • 250ML (8FL OZ) TOMATO JUICE • 150ML (5FL OZ) CARROT JUICE • SALT • BLACK PEPPER • GROUND CUMIN • LIME JUICE • 2 SLICES OF LIME

Combine the yoghurt with the tomato and carrot juices in a mixer and beat for a few seconds. Flavour the drink with salt, pepper, a pinch of cumin, and a dash of lime juice and pour into glasses. Serve garnished with a slice of lime.

PER DRINK: 143 kcal • 4 g protein • 1 g fat • 10 g carbohydrate

Iced Pineapple and

an exotic burst of vitamins

Almond Shake

Peel the pineapple, removing the brown "eyes". Cut the fruit into four lengthwise and remove the hard core from the segments. Roughly chop the fruit and place in a mixer.

FOR 2 GLASSES:
1/2 SMALL RIPE PINEAPPLE
1/2 LIME
1 TBSP BROWN SUGAR
1 TBSP UNSWEETENED ALMOND PUREE (FROM HEALTH FOOD STORES)
75G (3OZ) FROZEN YOGHURT
CRUSHED ICE
1 SMALL KIWI
FRESH MINT

Squeeze the lime juice and add to the pineapple with the sugar and almond puree. Puree until smooth. Add the frozen yoghurt and mix again briefly. Divide the crushed ice between tall glasses and top with the drink. Cut the kiwi (peeled or unpeeled) into segments or thick slices. Decorate the shakes with the slices of kiwi and mint leaves.

Pineapple

This exotic fruit is simply puréed for this recipe, so its levels of vitamins A, B, and C are retained. The flesh contains bromelin, an enzyme which separates protein in the body and thus stimulates the digestion of protein. Incidentally, this enzyme is also responsible for the incompatibility between fresh pineapple and gelatine – it prevents the gelatine from setting. Because pineapple contains only a few calories, is diuretic and detoxifying, it is a useful part of any diet.

PER DRINK:

167 kcal

5 g protein

6 g fat

25 g carbohydrate

power

Index to recipes

Vitamin Diet - lose weight with fresh fruit and vegetables

Asparagus **19**
Carrot crèpes with asparagus 41
Raw asparagus salad 19

Bananas **55**
Blueberry and banana milk 55

Beansprouts
Curried ginger vegetables 33
Exotic sprout salad 12

Beetroot salad 20

Blueberries **55**
Blueberry and banana milk 55
Mixed berries 47
Raspberry and strawberry shake 56
Strawberry and kiwi salad 48

Broccoli
Cauliflower and broccoli salad 13
Stir-fried Thai vegetables 43

Brussels sprouts salad with pears 21

Buttermilk
Jellied buttermilk soup 50

Carrots
Carrot crèpes with asparagus filling 41
Curried ginger vegetables 33
Fruity raw carrot 20
Tomato and carrot yoghurt 57

Cauliflower and broccoli salad 13

Citrus fruits **52**
Citrus fruit platter 52

Cold vegetable soup 26
Coleslaw with red onions 17
Courgette and tomato salad 14
Cream of radish soup 29

Cucumber
Fruity cucumber drink 57

Curried ginger vegetables 33

Dates
Date and pineapple salad 48

Exotic sprout salad 12

Fruity cucumber drink 57
Fruity raw carrots 20

Grapefruit
Citrus fruit platter 52

Grapes **53**
Tea jelly with grapes 53

Green cabbage **17**
Coleslaw with red onions 17

Ham
Salsify and ham ragout 38

Iced pineapple and almond shake 58
Indonesian vegetable soup 27

Jellied buttermilk soup 50

Kiwi **49**
Melon and mango soup with kiwi 49
Strawberry and kiwi salad 48

Light minestrone 25
Light tortilla 35
Linguine with raw tomato sauce 44

Mango **49**
Melon and mango soup with kiwi 49

Melon **49**
Melon and mango soup with kiwi 49

Mixed berries 47

Orange
Citrus fruit platter 52
Spinach salad with orange 11

Abbreviations

tsp = teaspoon
tbsp = tablespoon

Pak choi
Stir-fried Thai vegetables   43

Pepper (capsicum)
Provençal peppers   36

Pineapple   **58**
Iced pineapple and almond shake   58
Date and pineapple salad   48

Plums   50
Jellied buttermilk soup   50

Potatoes
Light tortilla   35

Provençal peppers   36

Radish   **22**
Cream of radish soup   29
Stove-top spelt cakes with radishes   39
Vegetable vitamins   22

Raspberries   **56**
Raspberry and strawberry shake   56

Raw asparagus salad   19

Salsify   **38**
Salsify and ham ragout   38

Sauerkraut salad with chive cream   31
Spinach salad with orange   11

Sprouts   **12**
Exotic sprout salad   11

Stir-fried pumpkin with brown rice   34
Stir-fried Thai vegetables   43
Stove-top spelt cakes with radishes   39

Strawberries
Raspberry and strawberry shake   56
Strawberry and kiwi salad   48

Swede   **30**
Swede stew with tartare dumplings   30

Tea jelly with grapes   53
Tomatoes
Courgette and tomato salad   14
Linguine with raw tomato sauce   44
Tomato and carrot yoghurt   57

Turnips   **30**
Turnip and turkey fricassee   42

Vegetable stock   13
Vegetable vitamins   22
Vegetables and herb salad   16

Most of the ingredients required for the recipes in this book are easily available from supermarkets and health food stores. In case of difficulty, contact the following importers of organic German produce:-
The Organic Food Company, Unit 2, Blacknest Industrial Estate, Blacknest Road, Alton GU34 4PX
(T) 01420 520530   (F) 01420 23985

Windmill Organics, 66 Meadow Close, London SW20 9JD
(T) 0181 395 9749   (F) 0181 286 4732

Fermented Wheat Juice is produced in Germany by Kanne Brottrunk GMBH
(T) 00 49 2592 97400   (F) 00 49 2592 61370

Further information on German food importers is available from The Central Marketing Organisation
(T) 0181 944 0484   (F) 0181 944 0441

Caution

The techniques and recipes in this book
are to be used at the reader's sole
discretion and risk.
Always consult a doctor if you are in doubt
about a medical condition.

Angelika Ilies

Angelika, who was born in Hamburg,
studied ecotrophology and then began her
career in London, where she experienced
working life in a renowned publishing
house. Back in her own country, she added
her support to Germany's leading food
magazine. Since 1989 she has enjoyed a
successful career as a freelance writer and
food journalist.

Photos: FoodPhotography Eising, Munich

Susie M. and **Pete Eising** have studios in
Munich and Kennebunkport, Maine/USA.
They studied at the Munich Academy of
Photography, where they established their
own studio for food photography in 1991.

Food styling: **Monika Schuster**

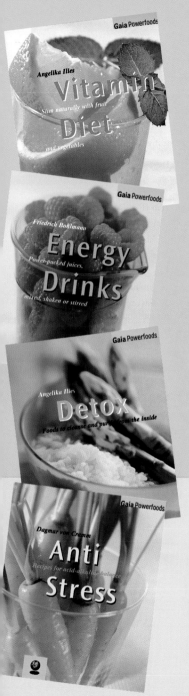

Vitamin Diet

Lose weight naturally with fresh fruit and vegetables
Angelika Ilies
£4.99
ISBN 1 85675 145 7
All the benefits of eating fresh fruit and vegetables plus a natural way to weight loss.

Energy Drinks

Power-packed juices, mixed, shaken or stirred
Friedrich Bohlmann
£4.99
ISBN 1 85675 140 6
Fresh juices packed full of goodness for vitality and health

Detox

Foods to cleanse and purify from within
Angelika Ilies
£4.99
ISBN 1 85675 150 3
Detoxify your body as part of your daily routine by eating nutritional foods that have cleansing properties

Anti Stress

Recipes for Acid-Alkaline Balance
Dagmar von Cramm
£4.99
ISBN 1 85675 155 4
A balanced diet to reduce stress levels, maximise immunity and help you keep fit

For a catalogue of titles please call 01453 752985 or visit our website www.gaiabooks.co.uk